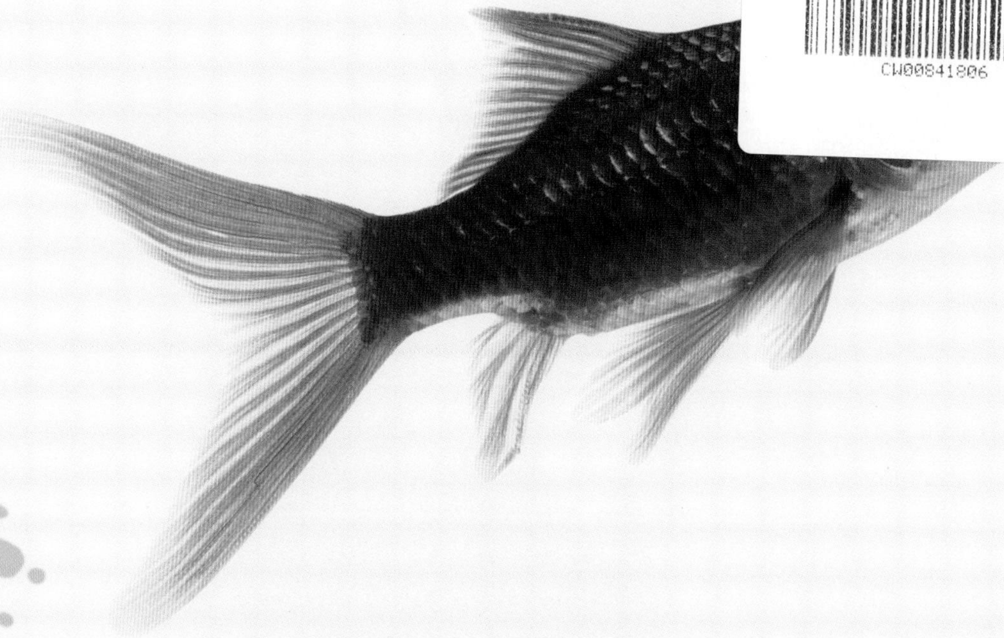

A fish can swim.

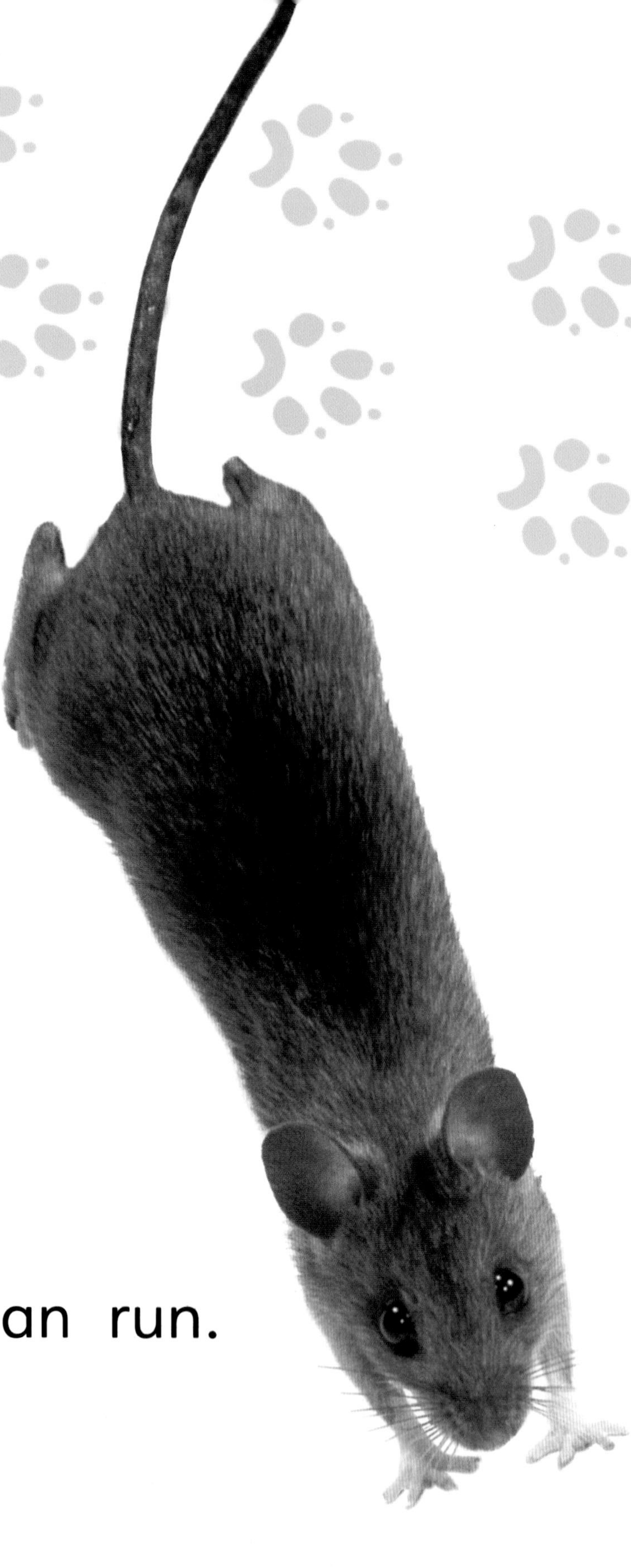

A mouse can run.

Hop, Swim and Run

Margaret Clyne

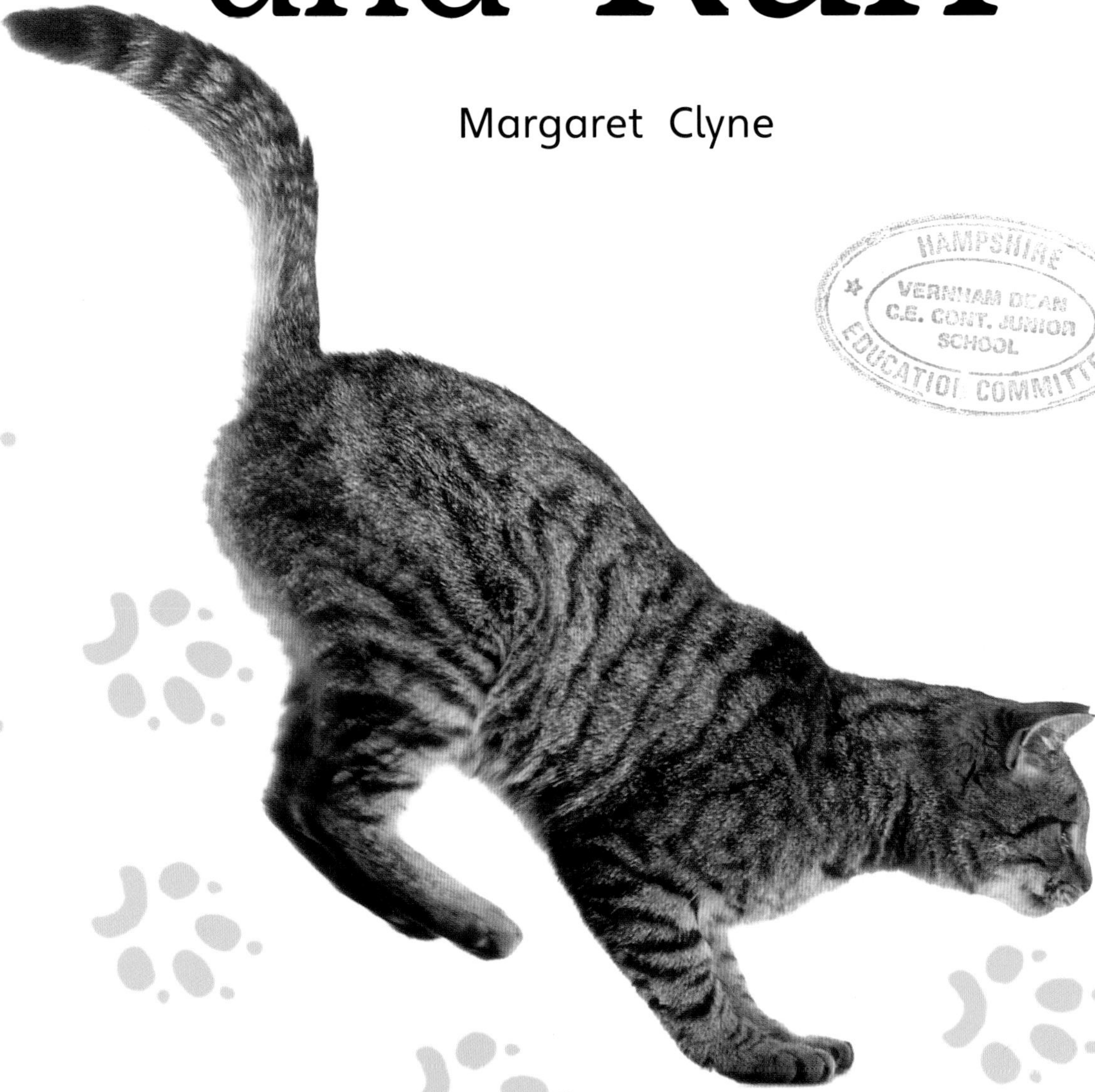

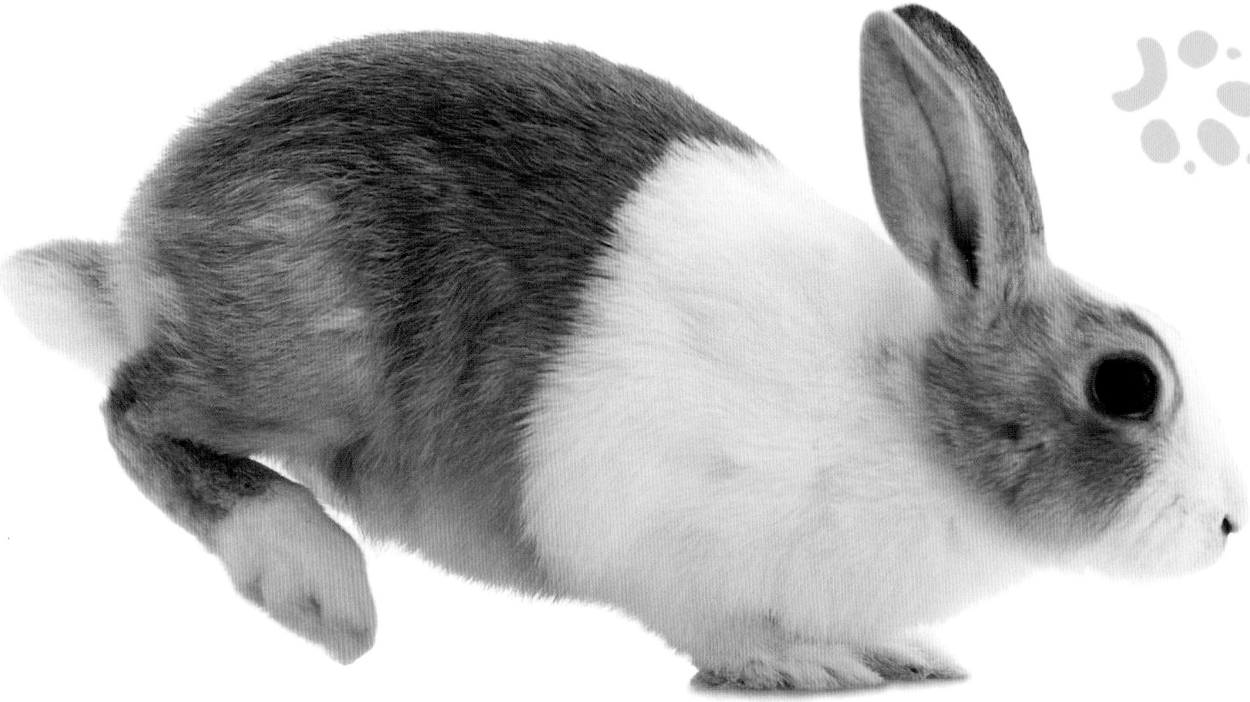

A rabbit can hop.

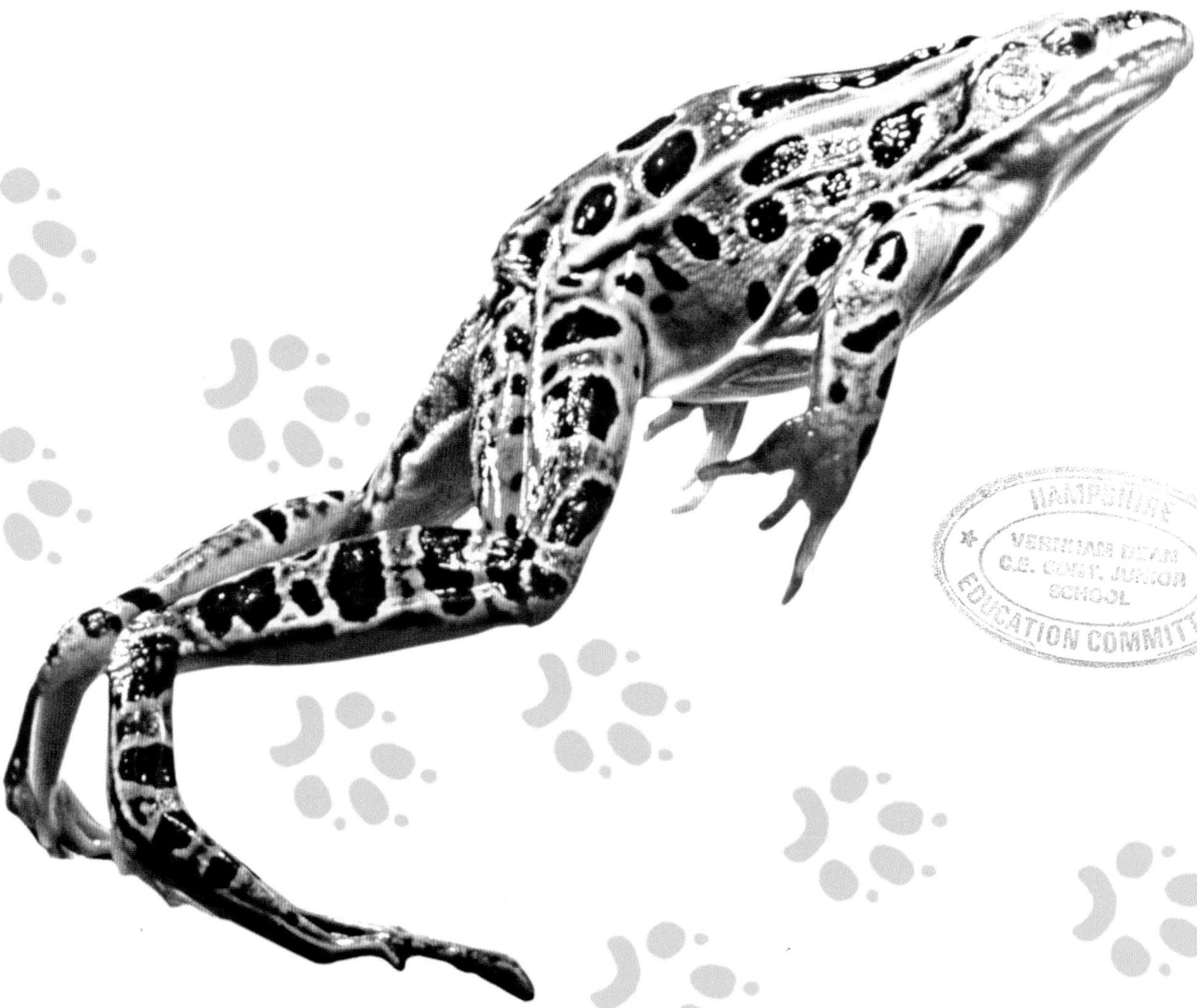

A frog can hop.

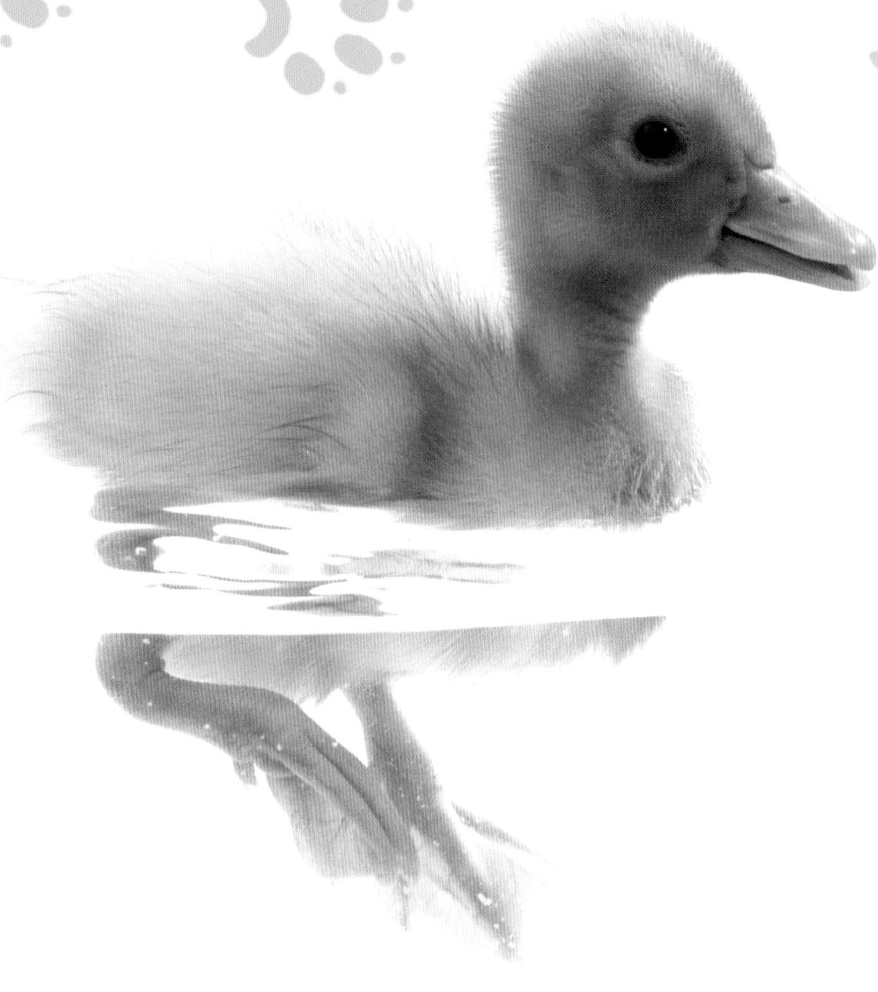

A duck can swim.

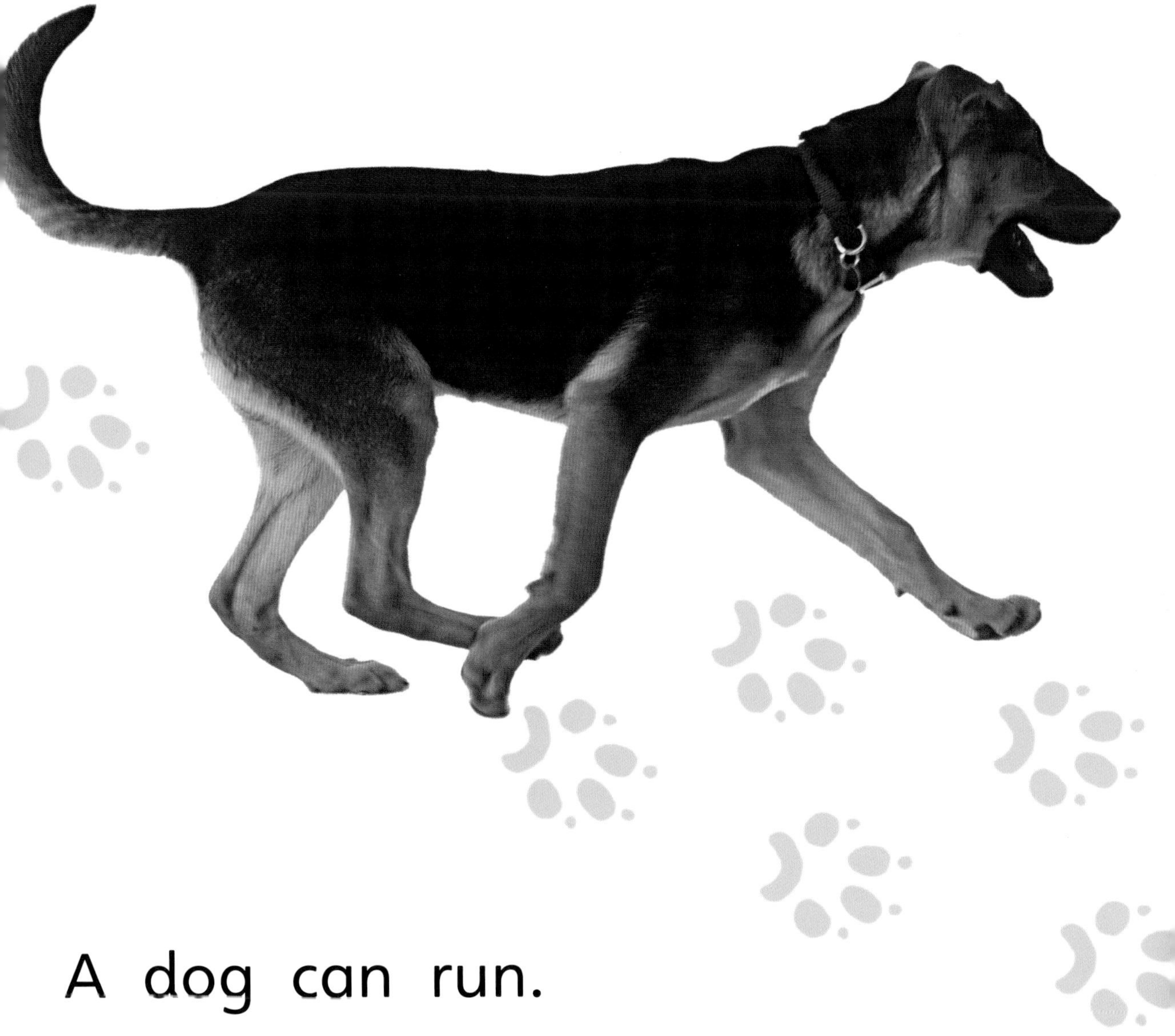

A dog can run.

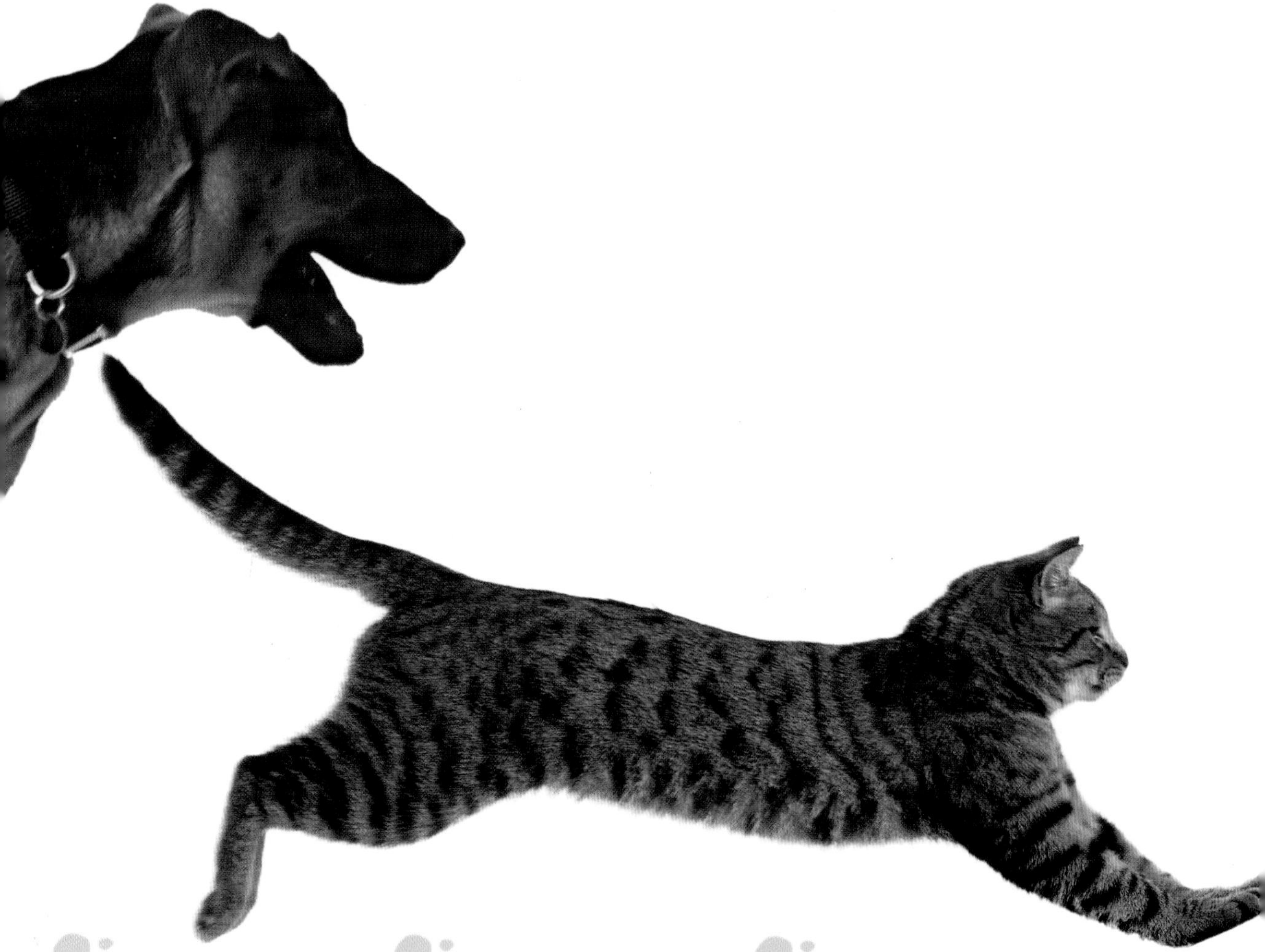

But a cat can run and run!